EVERYBODY NEEDS A TURN

A Book for Brothers and Sisters of Children With Speech and Language Disorders

Written by Denise Underkoffler, MA, CCC-SLP

Illustrations by Lindsay Dale-Scott

ASHA **Press**

PREFACE

Sometimes, brothers and sisters feel left out when their sibling is getting more attention. This may happen when a sibling is getting speech and language services. This book is meant to help these brothers and sisters understand and participate in speech-language therapy and practice time.

I know about this issue because I am a sibling of a sister who stutters, the mother of a child with a speech and language disorder, and a speech-language pathologist (SLP).

- **My sister** had a stuttering problem and had difficulty getting her words out. I often felt helpless as I watched her struggle to talk. I worried about her and sometimes felt guilty because I could talk so effortlessly.

- **As a mother**, I realized our daughter sometimes felt her needs were not as important as our son's. Our son received various services for communication and health problems. Our daughter competed for our time and attention.

- **As an SLP**, I've had many experiences with children whose siblings were affected by their brother's or sister's speech-language disorder. I worked with a child who was nonverbal whose sibling stopped talking. His brother got to play games during therapy sessions several times a week. The sessions looked like fun and he wanted to participate, too. I've also seen siblings of children with a communication disorder develop disruptive behaviors to gain their parent's attention.

Sometimes, siblings feel like they are less important to the family. Parents should reassure them and let them know they are valued and loved. Parents and SLPs need to remember "Everybody Needs a Turn" to participate in family activities and even speech-language sessions when possible.

This book includes communication tips that involve the whole family.
We all need to know that we hold a special place within our family and we each deserve to get our turn.

I dedicate this book to the memory of my son, Chad.
His positive attitude, perseverance, and gentle spirit continue
to inspire me and many others every day.

Hanna loves to talk, sing, play dress-up, and put on shows for her family. Her Mommy calls her a "chatterbox" because Hanna talks all day long.

Her little brother, Peter, is very quiet and doesn't like to talk. People have trouble understanding him. He likes to color and build. Daddy calls Peter an "expert builder" because he builds very big castles and bridges.

Some days, Peter goes to see Ms.Tepper.
Mommy said Ms.Tepper helps Peter learn to
talk better. Peter loves to see Ms.Tepper because
he gets to play fun games while he practices talking.

Sometimes, Hanna has to sit in a room with a
woman at a desk and wait. Mommy or Daddy and
Peter visit with Ms.Tepper. Hanna doesn't like waiting.

One day at Ms.Tepper's, Hanna asked Mommy, "When is it my turn to play with Ms.Tepper?" Mommy said, "Ms.Tepper helps make talking easier for Peter. You don't need help talking, my sweet Hanna. You talk and sing all day long! You have books to read while you wait." Hanna felt disappointed.

That night, Hanna was ready with her favorite book for story time. But Mommy was helping Peter practice his words. She had to wait again. Hanna was mad. She didn't want to wait for her story time. She yelled, "I don't WANT to wait! It's MY turn now." She ran into her room and knocked over Peter's castle.

Mommy and Daddy came into Hanna's room and gave her a hug. "We know it's hard to wait for your turn," they said. "But, we all need to help each other. It's part of being in a family. Sometimes, that means waiting to take your turn."

"Right now, Peter needs some extra help with his talking," Mommy explained. "He's just as important as you. We love you both very much. You'll always get your turn too."

Daddy said, "Sometimes, you are the one getting a turn, and Peter is waiting." Hanna thought about that. "Oh, yeah, like during my dance class."

The next day, Mommy told Hanna, "Ms. Tepper says you can be Peter's 'talking buddy.' She thinks it's fun to take turns talking—**everybody needs a turn!**" Hanna was happy to help her brother and have her own turn to talk.

Mommy said, "It's time for Peter to practice his words."
She asked Hanna to join their game. First, Peter practiced
some words. Next, Peter and Hanna took turns talking about
their favorite things. They took turns asking and answering
questions. Sometimes, Hanna answered in funny voices.
That made Peter laugh.

Hanna said she liked being Peter's talking buddy.
She asked Peter to be her "building buddy."
Hanna said, "I like when you help me build!"

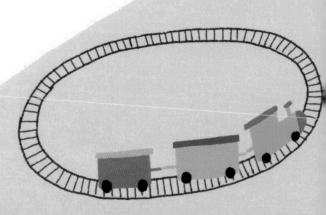

From then on, Hanna liked going to Ms.Tepper's with Peter. Ms.Tepper had a "talking stick" they passed around. Whoever held the talking stick got to talk. Everyone else had to be quiet and wait. Sometimes, Peter needed more time to talk, and Hanna had to wait. Ms.Tepper called this a turn-taking game! Mommy said they could play the game at home with Daddy, too.

Hanna and Peter had fun being each other's buddy. After a while, it was easier for Peter to talk, and he didn't have to go to Ms.Tepper's as often. Hanna was proud of Peter for working so hard at talking. Waiting became a little easier for Hanna. She knew that even if she had to wait, sooner or later,

everybody gets a turn!

TEN TIPS TO ENHANCE COMMUNICATION WITH YOUR WHOLE FAMILY

TIP 1. Talk to your child's speech-language pathologist (SLP) about the benefits of including siblings in speech and language treatment sessions. Discuss ways they can help. Participating during sessions and being involved with home practice are ways to ensure siblings don't feel left out. They want their turn!

TIP 2. Celebrate progress in speech and language treatment, and include siblings when possible. Celebrate each child's unique successes, like when a sibling learns to ride a bike, gets a good grade, or shows kindness to another person.

TIP 3. Set aside time for each child by scheduling a "date" to do something fun together (even if it is only for 10 minutes). Do a craft project, play a game, cook dinner, read favorite books, put a puzzle together, listen to and sing favorite songs.

TIP 4. For older siblings, talk openly about the communication challenges that their younger brother or sister faces. Encourage siblings to share their feelings about their sibling's challenges. **Here are some ideas to start the conversation:**

- What do you like to talk about with your brother/sister?
- Do you have any questions about the way your brother/sister talks?
- How do you feel when you have to wait for your brother/sister to...(practice their words, attend therapy sessions, etc.)?
- What can we do to make the waiting easier for you?

TIP 5. Help each child to feel heard and understood. Ask each child, "Is there something special you'd like to do as a family or on your own?"

TIP 6. Remind your child not to talk for their brother or sister who has the speech-language problem. Speaking for them can add more pressure.

TIP 7. Remind family members that they all need to take turns talking and listening. Occasionally ask children to hold a toy microphone, "talking stick," or any object they choose to signal that it's their turn to talk. It doesn't matter what they hold. The point is to remind children when it is their turn to talk and when it is their turn to listen.

TIP 8. Let your children know that they are each special to you and that you value them for their unique strengths and interests.

TIP 9. Seek help if you have concerns about your children's developmental milestones.

TIP 10. Be sure to take care of yourself, too! Being a parent is hard work. Find time for yourself, and learn some techniques to relieve stress and rejuvenate: Take a walk outside, exercise, learn yoga, meditate, practice mindfulness. Teach your children some of these same techniques.

QUESTIONS ABOUT THE STORY

Use these additional questions to start a discussion to help children relate to the characters in the book. It might help them open up and talk about their own feelings. Ask questions that are age-appropriate.

Q What is the story about?

Q Who are the main characters in the book?

Q Why did Hanna kick the castle over? What do you think she is feeling?

Q How does Hanna feel when she has to wait?

Q Do you ever feel the same way Hanna feels?

Q What can you do when you feel like Hanna?

Q How do you think Peter felt when Hanna asked him to be her "building buddy?"

Q What kind of "buddy" can you be?

Q What kind of "buddy" do you need?

Q Why is it important for everyone to get their turn?

Q What can we learn from this story?

Acknowledgments

I would like to thank my dear family and friends for encouraging me to write this book. I especially thank my daughter Abby and my sister Diane for providing insight and support. Thank you to all of the ASHA staff members involved in producing the book. I appreciate their valuable help and support throughout this entire process. I am very grateful to ASHA Press for giving me the opportunity to share my book with others.

This book was written for all children out there that "need a turn."